WHEN I FIRST CAME
TO THIS LAND

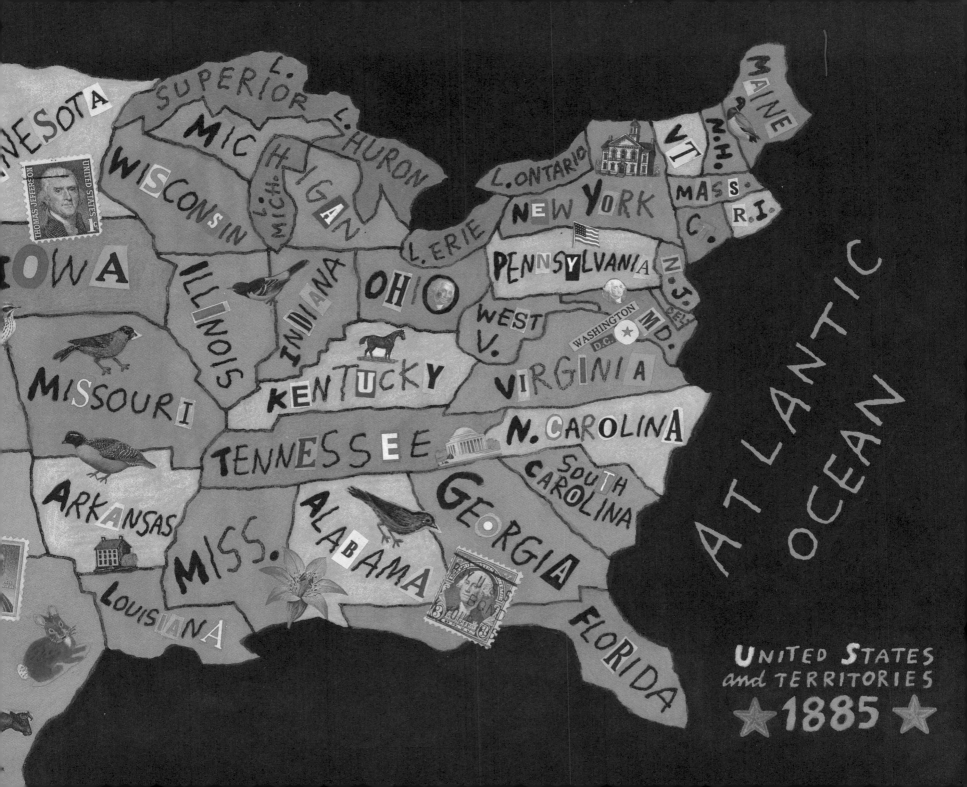

In memory of my grandparents,
who came here from Russia—HMZ

For Leon—ST

"When I First Came to This Land" was brought to Pennsylvania over a century ago by a German immigrant.
It appears in AND THE GREEN GRASS GREW ALL AROUND: FOLK POETRY FROM EVERYONE
by Alvin Schwartz (HarperCollins Publishers, 1992).

ISBN 0-439-05284-X

12 11 10 9 8 7 6 5 4 3 2 1   9/9 0 1 2 3 4/0

Printed in the U.S.A.   08

First Scholastic printing, March 1999

Text set in Cheltenham Bold

WHEN I FIRST CAME TO THIS LAND

RETOLD BY HARRIET ZIEFERT
PICTURES BY SIMMS TABACK

SCHOLASTIC INC.
New York Toronto London Auckland Sydney
Mexico City New Delhi Hong Kong

When I first came to this land,
I was not a wealthy man.

But the land was sweet and good,
And I did what I could.

I bought a farm.

And I called my farm
Muscle-in-my-arm!

I borrowed a plow.

I called my plow
Don't-know-how!
And I called my farm
Muscle-in-my-arm!

I bought a horse.

I called my horse
I'm-the-boss!
I called my plow
Don't-know-how!
And I called my farm
Muscle-in-my-arm!

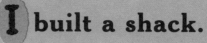**I** built a shack.

I called my shack
Break-my-back!
I called my horse
I'm-the-boss!
I called my plow
Don't-know-how!
And I called my farm
Muscle-in-my-arm!

I bought a cow.

I called my cow
No-milk-now!
I called my shack
Break-my-back!
I called my horse
I'm-the-boss!
I called my plow
Don't-know-how!
And I called my farm
Muscle-in-my-arm!

I bought a pig.

I called my pig
Too-darn-big!
I called my cow
No-milk-now!
I called my shack
Break-my-back!
I called my horse
I'm-the-boss!
I called my plow
Don't-know-how!
And I called my farm
Muscle-in-my-arm!

I found a wife.

I called my wife
Spice-of-my-life!
I called my pig
Too-darn-big!
I called my cow
No-milk-now!
I called my shack
Break-my-back!
I called my horse
I'm-the-boss!
I called my plow
Don't-know-how!
And I called my farm
Muscle-in-my-arm!

WANTED A WIFE,

I had a son.

I called my son
So-much-fun!
I called my wife
Spice-of-my-life!
I called my pig
Too-darn-big!
I called my cow
No-milk-now!
I called my shack
Break-my-back!
I called my horse
I'm-the-boss!
I called my plow
Don't-know-how!
And I called my farm
Muscle-in-my-arm!

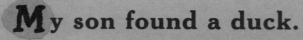**M**y son found a duck.

And he called his duck
Duck-Duck-Duck!
And he called his pa
Da-Da-Da!
And he called his ma
Ma-Ma-Ma!

When I first came to this land,
I was not a wealthy man.

But the land was sweet and good,
And I did what I could!

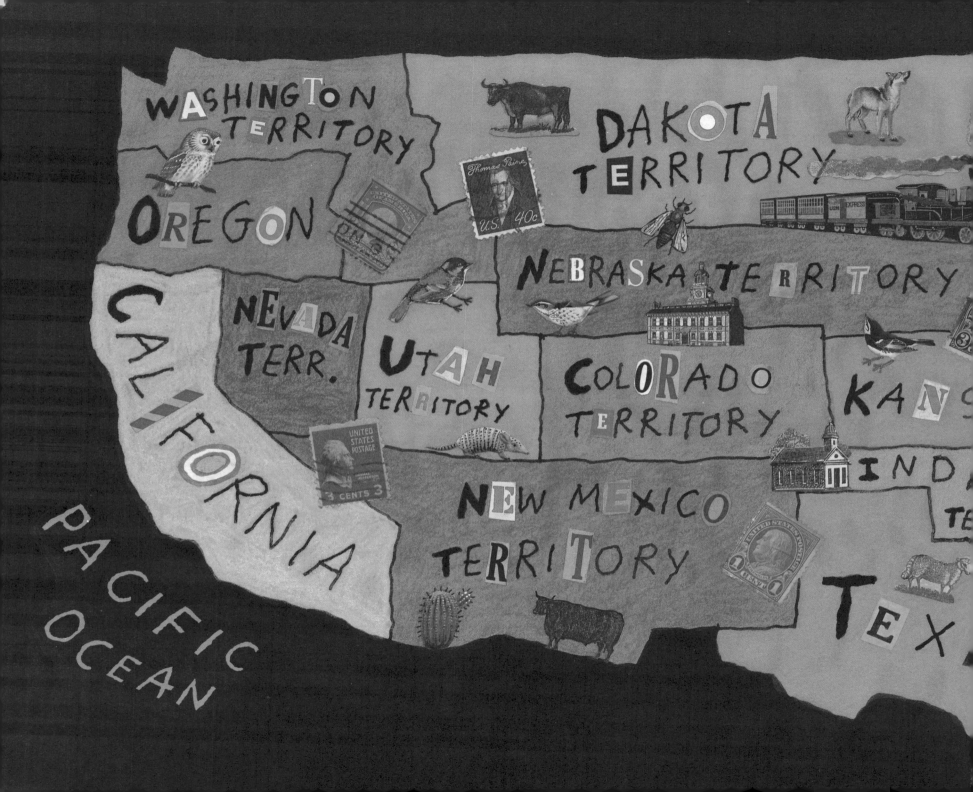

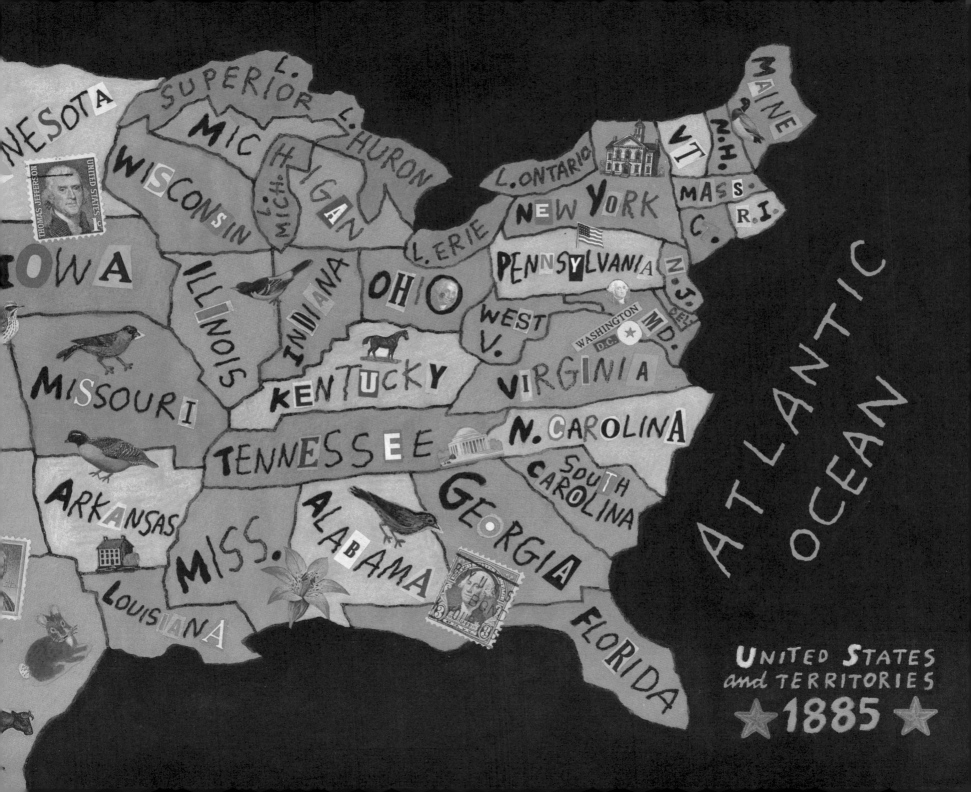